Mirror, Mirror

Description

Learners explore the phenomenon of seeing their reflections in some objects but not others. They learn that mirrors are the best objects for seeing themselves because they are shiny and flat. Then they explore how to redirect a light beam using flashlights and mirrors.

Alignment With the *Next Generation Science Standards*

Performance Expectations

1-PS4-2: Make observations to construct an evidence-based account that objects can be seen only when illuminated.

K-2-ETS1-2: Develop a simple sketch, drawing, or physical model to illustrate how the shape of an object helps it function as needed to solve a given problem.

Science and Engineering Practice	Disciplinary Core Ideas	Crosscutting Concept
Constructing Explanations and Designing Solutions Make observations (firsthand or from media) to construct an evidence-based account for natural phenomena. Use tools and materials provided to design a device that solves a specific problem.	PS4.B: Electromagnetic Radiation Objects can be seen if light is available to illuminate them or if they give off their own light. Mirrors can be used to redirect a light beam. ETS1.B: Developing Possible Solutions Designs can be conveyed through sketches, drawings, or physical models. These representations are useful in communicating ideas for a problem's solutions to other people.	Cause and Effect Simple tests can be designed to gather evidence to support or refute student ideas about causes.

Note: The activities in this lesson will help students move toward the performance expectations listed, which is the goal after multiple activities. However, the activities will not by themselves be sufficient to reach the performance expectations.

Featured Picture Books

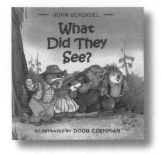

TITLE: *What Did They See?*
AUTHOR: **John Schindel**
ILLUSTRATOR: **Doug Cushman**
PUBLISHER: **Henry Holt**
YEAR: **2003**
GENRE: **Story**
SUMMARY: *Raccoon hurries to show Beaver, Porcupine, and Otter the most amazing "thingamajig" that they have ever seen (a mirror).*

TITLE: *I See Myself*
AUTHOR: **Vicki Cobb**
ILLUSTRATOR: **Julia Gorton**
PUBLISHER: **HarperCollins**
YEAR: **2002**
GENRE: **Non-Narrative Information**
SUMMARY: *Learn why you can see yourself in shiny objects with this fun, interactive book about light.*

Time Needed

This lesson will take several class periods. Suggested scheduling is as follows:

Session 1: Engage with What Did They See? Read-Aloud

Session 2: Explore/Explain with I See Myself Read-Aloud

Session 3: Elaborate with Mirror Challenges

Session 4: Evaluate with Light Up the Dark Cave

Materials

For What Did They See? Read-Aloud

- Plastic mirror hidden in a "mystery bag or box" with a large question mark on the front of the bag

For I See Myself Read-Aloud

- Small plastic mirror
- Small flashlight

For Mirror Challenges (per pair)

- Small plastic mirror
- Small flashlight

For Light Up the Dark Cave (per pair)

- Small flashlight (from the explore phase)
- Small plastic mirror (from the explore phase)

Ordering Information for Mirrors
Educational Innovations, Inc.
www.teachersource.com

National Science Teaching Association

- Mailing tube or paper towel tube with one end covered
- A figurine of a person that can fit in the tube (such as a LEGO figurine)

Student Pages

- Mirror Challenges
- Light Up the Dark Cave
- STEM Everywhere

Background

Light is an essential part of our everyday lives. Without light, we would not be able to see. This fact can be difficult for some students to believe, because most of us have never been in a completely dark place before. Light behaves according to special rules. For example, it always travels in a straight line until it hits something. When light hits a mirror, it reflects, or bounces off the surface. (Note: The book I See Myself uses the kid-friendly term bounce instead of the scientific term reflect. Technically speaking, light does not "bounce" in the same way that a ball bounces. Instead, light is actually absorbed by the molecules in the mirror and then sent back out as a reflection.) The light traveling in any one direction in a straight line is called a ray of light. A group of light rays given out from a source is called a beam of light.

The law of reflection states that, when something bounces off a perfectly flat surface, the angle at which it hits the surface will be equal to the angle at which it bounces away. A mirror reflects light in this way because of its very flat, smooth surface. A mirror is made of a glass sheet in front of a metallic coating where the reflection actually occurs. A curved mirror, like a fun house mirror, can be thought of as consisting of a very large number of small flat mirrors oriented at slightly different angles. The law of reflection still applies, but the image you see is distorted. A very shiny spoon can be used to demonstrate this type of distortion.

Light isn't just reflected off mirrors; light is reflected off every object you see. When light strikes a rough surface, it reflects off in many directions due to the microscopic irregularities of the surface. Thus, a mirror image is not formed. This is called diffuse reflection. As you are reading this, light is reflecting off the page. The black type on the page is absorbing all the light that hits it, but the rest of the page is reflecting light. The reflected light is scattering in many directions. Some of the scattered light reaches your eyes. That's why you can read this, but you can't see your reflection in the page.

In this lesson, students are engaged in the science and engineering practices (SEPs) of constructing explanations and designing solutions. Students make firsthand observations of how light behaves with flashlights and mirrors and develop explanations based on those observations. They compare their ideas to the information presented in a nonfiction book that explains the phenomenon they observed in a scientific way. Then they apply what they have learned about mirrors and light to solve a problem. The crosscutting concept (CCC) of cause and effect is highlighted in this lesson as students conduct simple tests with flashlights and mirrors to determine what happens when light strikes a mirror. They also learn that light allows us to see things, and without light we can't see anything. These simple concepts lay the foundation for later study about how vision works in the upper elementary grades.

Learning Progressions

Below are the disciplinary core idea (DCI) grade band endpoints for grades K–2 and 3–5. These are provided to show how student understanding of the DCIs in this lesson will progress in future grade levels.

DCIs	Grades K–2	Grades 3–5
PS4.B: Electromagnetic Radiation	• Objects can be seen only when light is available to illuminate them. Some objects give off their own light. • Some materials allow light to pass through them, others allow only some light through, and still others block all the light and create a dark shadow on any surface beyond them, where the light cannot reach. Mirrors can be used to redirect a beam of light.	• An object can be seen when light reflected from its surface enters the eyes.
ETS1.B: Developing Possible Solutions	• Designs can be conveyed through sketches, drawings, or physical models. These representations are useful for communicating ideas for a problem's solutions to other people.	• At whatever stage, communicating with peers about proposed solutions is an important part of the design process, and shared ideas can lead to improved designs.

Source: Willard, T., ed. (2015). The NSTA quick-reference guide to the NGSS: Elementary school. Arlington, VA: NSTA Press.

 # engage

What Did They See? Read-Aloud

> Connecting to the Common Core
> **Reading: Literature**
> KEY IDEAS AND DETAILS: 1.1, CRAFT AND STRUCTURE: 1.5

Note: If you are unable to locate a copy of What Did They See?, you can use a riddle to replace the read-aloud: "It is flat. It is shiny. It can follow your every move. It contains something lovely, good-looking, and amazing. What is it?" Then have students open the mystery bag or box to see the mirror.

 Inferring

Hold up the cover of the book What Did They See? Ask

? What do you think this book might be about? Why do you think so? (Answers will vary.)

? Do you think the book is fiction or nonfiction? (Fiction.) How can you tell? (Possible answers include that it has cartoon animals on the cover, and the animals are wearing clothing.)

ing," "good-looking," or "lovely"? (They were seeing themselves in the mirror.)

? How do you know this book is fiction? (Possible answers include animals can't really talk, and they don't wear clothes.)

explore/explain

I See Myself Read-Aloud

Stop-and-Try-It

Connecting to the Common Core
Reading: Informational Text
KEY IDEAS AND DETAILS: 1.1

> **SEP: Constructing Explanations and Designing Solutions**
> Make observations to construct an evidence-based account for natural phenomena.

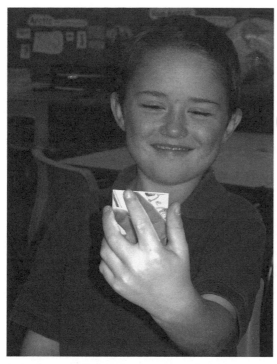

LOOKING AT THE "AMAZING THINGAMABOB"

Questioning

Read What Did They See? to the class. Model the thinking of a good reader by saying aloud "I wonder what it could be?" when appropriate in the story. Before you reveal the final page of the book, tell students that the "good-looking thingamajig, lovely whatchamacallit, dashing thingamabob" from the story is inside the mystery bag! Ask if anyone wants to look inside the bag. Make them promise not to tell what the mystery object is, but each time someone looks in the bag, repeat the line from the book, "and what each one saw was something wonderful indeed." After several students have peeked in the bag and the suspense has been built, reveal the contents of the bag … a mirror! Ask

? What wonderful thing do you see when you look at the amazing "thingamabob"? (myself)

? Why did each character in the story think that what they saw was so "dashing," "amaz-

The book I See Myself has a unique format. The author, Vicki Cobb, wrote it in a way that encourages readers to "stop and try it." In the "Note to the Reader" at the beginning of the book, she explains that the best way to use this book is to have children do the activities as they come up, step away from the book, and come back to it after the child has made the discovery. You may want to mark the stopping points with sticky notes beforehand to remind you when to pause and try the activity or ask questions.

Read pages 2 and 3 of the book, which ends with the following: "Now suppose there were no mirrors in the world. What could you do to see yourself?"

Stop reading, and invite students to walk around the room silently to discover if they can

see themselves in anything. Point out some things for students to look into such as a picture frame, a door knob, windows, the pencil sharpener, and so on. Students are often surprised to learn that they can see themselves in many things in the classroom! Have students return to your reading area, and then ask

? In what things could you see yourself? (Answers include metal objects, doorknobs, the glass in a picture frame, and windows.)

? What do these things have in common? (Answers include they are smooth, and they are shiny.)

? Did you appear as clear in these objects as you appeared in the mirror? (no)

? Why do you think the mirror was best for seeing yourself? (Answers will vary.)

Continue reading the book; stop reading after the part on page 11 that says, "Can you see yourself in the dark?" Ask

? Have any of you ever been in a completely dark place? (Answers will vary.)

? Do you think it is possible to see yourself in a mirror in the dark? (Answers will vary.)

Read the following pages that explain that you can't see ANYTHING in the dark. In order to see, you must have light. Continue reading and stop reading after page 10, which asks, "Can you aim the light where you want it to go?"

Show students a small mirror and a flashlight. Ask for a volunteer to hold the mirror and another volunteer to hold the flashlight. Challenge the two to use the mirror to aim the light from the flashlight to light up something you choose on the wall or something you place on the floor. Allow other pairs to try.

Connecting to the Common Core
Reading: Informational Text
INTEGRATION OF KNOWLEDGE AND IDEAS: 1.7

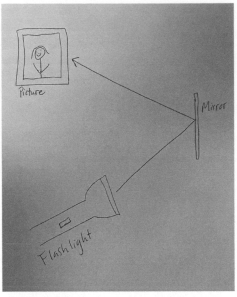

LABELED DIAGRAM

As you read pages 20–28, point out how the illustrator uses lines to show how the ball bounces and to show how light bounces. Turn back to pages 18–19 and point out how the illustrator shows light bouncing with the arrangement of the words on the page. Tell students that scientists often use arrows to represent light in their diagrams and drawings. Show an example on the board by drawing and labeling a picture that represents the light from the flashlight being redirected to light up a picture on the wall. Explain that light traveling in any one direction in a straight line is called a ray of light. A group of light rays given out from a source is called a beam of light.

Read the rest of the book aloud. After reading, ask

? Why are mirrors the best objects for seeing yourself? (because they are flat and shiny)

? In order to see yourself, in order to see anything, you must have what? (light)

? When a ray of light hits a mirror, what happens? (It makes a perfect "bounce" every time.)

? Why can't you see yourself in a sweater or in the pages of a book? (A sweater or page is not perfectly flat and shiny. The light reflects off the sweater or page and scatters in many directions.)

National Science Teaching Association

elaborate

Mirror Challenges

> **CCC: Cause and Effect**
> Simple tests can be designed to gather evidence to support or refute student ideas about causes.

Give each pair of students a mirror and a flashlight for this activity. Make your room as dark as possible. Have students shine the flashlight on the mirror and observe where the beam of light goes. Ask

? Does the light from the flashlight go through the mirror? (No. It bounces off.)

? Where does the light go after it bounces off the mirror? (Answers might include behind me and on the wall.)

Keep the room darkened, and give each student the Mirror Challenges student page. Have students put a checkmark in each box as they complete challenges 1–4. (They can use their flashlights to view their papers.) As they are working, circulate to ask questions such as the following:

? How does the position of the mirror affect the direction the light goes?

? Where did you place the mirror to complete the challenge?

Mirror challenges

? What happens when you aim the mirror the other way?

Turn the lights back on, and have students complete number 5 where they draw a labeled diagram of one of the challenges.

After students have completed the Mirror Challenges student page, ask

? Were you able to do all of the challenges?

? Did you get them all on the first try?

? Which one was the most difficult? Why?

? Did any of the results surprise you? Why?

Invite students to share their diagrams and explain their thinking. Ask

? What did we use to represent a ray of light in our diagram? (an arrow)

Reread the part of page 25 of I See Myself that says, "When a ray of light strikes a mirror, it makes a perfect bounce." Remind students that ray refers to the straight-line path that light takes when it travels. Continue reading, "A mirror handles a gazillion rays of light at once. And every one makes a perfect bounce every time." Remind students that the group of "a gazillion" rays coming from the flashlight together are called a beam of light. Tell students that when describing light, scientists usually use the word reflection instead of bounce. Reflect means to bounce back. Reflection is the act of bouncing back. Read the page again, this time substituting the word reflection for the word bounce each time it appears on the page.

Ask

? Do you think you could see your reflection in the mirror if this room were completely dark? (Answers will vary.)

Challenge students to try this at home with adult supervision:

Take a flashlight and a small hand mirror into a room with no windows, such as a closet or bathroom. Shut the door, and cover the cracks below the door with towels. Then turn off the light and the flashlight. Look into the mirror. What can you see? (Explain that, if the room were completely dark, there would be no light to reflect. In fact, you cannot see anything without light.)

evaluate

Light Up the Dark Cave

> **SEP: Constructing Explanations and Designing Solutions**
> Use tools and materials provided to design a device that solves a specific problem.

Tell students that caves are among the darkest places in the natural world. Ask

? Have any of you been in a cave before? If so, what was it like? (Answers will vary.)

Show students the Wild Kratts video "To the Bat Cave" listed in the "Website" section at the end of this lesson. This short video clip shows the Kratt brothers exploring a cave looking for bats.

After the video, ask

? What is it like inside a cave? (dark, wet)

? How did the Kratt brothers see in the cave? (They wore helmets with lights on them.)

Point out that the farther you go into a cave, the darker it gets. Once you get to the point that sunlight can't reach you, it is so dark you can't see anything at all. Tell students that you have a challenge for them. Show them a figurine of a person and tell them that this represents a cave explorer. Show them a cardboard tube (with one end closed off) laying on its side and tell them it represents a cave. Hold up a flashlight and explain that it represents the Sun. Turn the flashlight on. Hold it above the tube at an angle so that the entrance to the cave (opening of the container) is lit up, but the rest of the tube is dark.

Then share that the "explorer" has gone deep into the cave (all the way to the end of the container) when suddenly his flashlight burns out. It is totally dark because the sunlight can't reach that far. Without light, the explorer can't see anything! Tell students that their challenge is to use a mirror to light the way for the explorer to find his way out of the cave. To support them as they design their solutions, you may want to have students think back to their previous experiences during the Mirror Challenges. Ask

? What happens when light hits a mirror? (It bounces off.)

? How can you use a mirror to make light go where you want it to go? (Shine the flashlight on the mirror and move the mirror around.)

After sharing this scenario, divide students into pairs and have them set up the scene using their supplies. The cardboard tube goes on its side, the figurine is placed at the closed end of the container, and the flashlight is held up at an angle so just the entrance of the cave is lit.

Writing

Connecting to the Common Core
Writing
RESEARCH TO BUILD KNOWLEDGE: 1.8

Have students experiment with the position of the mirror until the figurine at the end of the container is illuminated. Then give each student the Light Up the Dark Cave student page. Have them draw the configuration that worked for them. They should include labels on their drawings (cave, Sun, explorer, mirror) and use arrows to represent the light rays. Students' drawings should show the "Sun" above the open end of the tube and a mirror directing the light inside the tube to light up the explorer. Students should represent the light beam with straight arrows reflecting off the mirror.

LIGHTING UP THE DARK CAVE

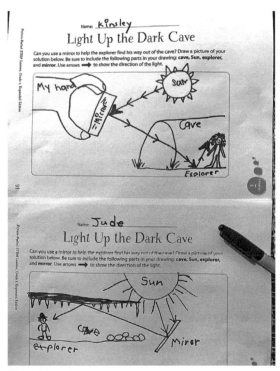

STUDENT DRAWINGS

STEM Everywhere

Give students the STEM Everywhere student page as a way to involve their families and extend their learning. They can do the activity with an adult helper and share their results with the class. If students do not have access to the internet or materials at home, you may choose to have them complete this activity at school.

Opportunities for Differentiated Instruction

This box lists questions and challenges related to the lesson that students may select to research, investigate, or innovate. Students may also use the questions as examples to help them generate their own questions. These questions can help you move your students from the teacher-directed investigation to engaging in the science and engineering practices in a more student-directed format.

Extra Support

For students who are struggling to meet the lesson objectives, provide a question and guide them in the process of collecting research or helping them design procedures or solutions.

Extensions

For students with high interest or who have already met the lesson objectives, have them choose a question (or pose their own question), conduct their own research, and design their own procedures or solutions.

After selecting one of the questions in this box or formulating their own questions, students can individually or collaboratively make predictions, design investigations or surveys to test their predictions, collect evidence, devise explanations, design solutions, or examine related resources. They can communicate their findings through a science notebook, at a poster session or gallery walk, or by producing a media project.

Research

Have students brainstorm researchable questions:

? What are mirrors made of?

? How do fun house mirrors work?

? How does a disco ball work?

Investigate

Have students brainstorm testable questions to be solved through science or math:

? How can you use two mirrors to see the back of your head?

? What happens when you write your name on a piece of paper and look at it in the mirror?

? What does your reflection look like on the inside of a metal spoon compared to the outside of a spoon?

Continued

Opportunities for Differentiated Instruction (*continued*)

Innovate
Have students brainstorm problems to be solved through engineering:

? Can you design a miniature fun house using a box, spoons, and mirrors?

? Can you create a light maze with multiple mirrors?

? Can you use mirrors to design a device that will allow you to see around corners?

Website

 "To the Bat Cave" video from *Wild Kratts* on PBS
https://www.pbslearningmedia.org/resource/3d3c45c1-f85e-4bf2-be14-45e021866679/3d3c45c1-f85e-4bf2-be14-45e021866679

More Books to Read

Pfeffer, W. 2015. *Light is all around us.* New York: HarperCollins.
Summary: From the Let's Read-and-Find-Out series, this book introduces different light sources.

Rosinsky, N. M. 2002 *Light: Shadows, mirrors, and rainbows.* Minneapolis: Picture Window Books.
Summary: Simple text and fun, colorful illustrations help readers understand how shadows are made, how mirrors work, how rainbows are made, and more. Includes simple experiments, a table of contents and glossary, and a website with links to other safe, fun websites related to the book's content.

Yolen, J. 2019. *A mirror to nature: Poems about reflections.* Honesdale, PA: Wordsong.
Summary: Jason Stemple's stunning photographs of the watery reflections of animals accompany 12 reflective poems by Jane Yolen.

Name: _____

Mirror Challenges

Put a check mark in the box ☑ after you complete each challenge.

☐ 1. Using the mirror, make your light shine on the wall behind you.

☐ 2. Using the mirror, make your light shine on the ceiling.

☐ 3. Using the mirror, make your light shine on your shirt.

☐ 4. Join another team, and make your light bounce off of two mirrors at the same time.

☐ 5. In the space below, draw a picture that shows what happens to light when it hits a mirror. Be sure to include the mirror and flashlight in your picture. Use arrows to show where the light goes.

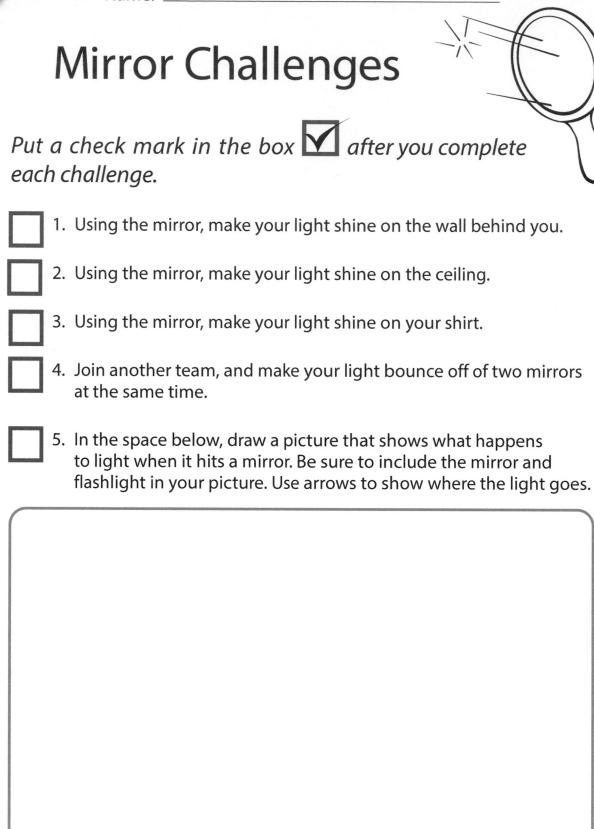

National Science Teaching Association

Name: _____

Light Up the Dark Cave

Can you use a mirror to help the explorer find their way out of the cave? Draw a picture of your solution below. Be sure to include the following parts in your drawing: **cave, Sun, explorer,** and **mirror.** Use arrows ⬆ to show the direction of the light.

Name: _____

STEM Everywhere

Dear Families,

At school, we have been learning about **light and reflections.** We used mirrors to change the direction of a beam of light from a flashlight. To find out more, ask your learner questions and discuss their answers:

- What did you learn?

- What was your favorite part of the lesson?

- What are you still wondering?

At home, you can watch a video together titled "Recycled Reflections" that shows how to use objects besides mirrors (some from the recycle bin) to redirect a beam of light to light up a wall, the ceiling, or even a friend.

 Scan the QR code or go to *www.pbslearningmedia.org/resource/ buac18-k2-sci-ps-reflections/recycled-reflections.*

After watching the video, see if you can find some things around your house that will redirect light. You can use a flashlight or sunlight. Together, write and draw what you discovered. Safety note: To prevent an eye injury, remind your learner not to look directly at sunlight or reflect it on a mirror into the eyes.

National Science Teaching Association